Comedy comic champions Beano and The Dandy weren't the
only humour comics to be produced by DC Thomson. Since
the launch of The Dandy in December 1937, and Beano in July
1938, several other comedy titles were released with many
of the artists sharing their chucklesome talents across the
smorgasbord of side-splitting strips inside.

So, take a leisurely, albeit riotous, stroll down memory lane
as we take you from Dudley D Watkins to Nigel Parkinson,
The Beezer to Sparky, Nutty, and Hoot. With so many comedy
legends to choose from, we're bound to have something that'll
have you chortling with our chums!

© DCT Consumer Products (UK) Ltd 2019
D.C. Thomson and Co. Ltd,
185 Fleet Street,
London EC4A 2HS

Printed in the EU

Dudley D Watkins

The grandaddy of them all, Dudley D Watkins was the quintessential artist of DC Thomson's comics. From The Broons to Lord Snooty, Watkins' heap of talent made him one of their most enduring artists.

LORD SNOOTY AND HIS PALS

While Dudley D Watkins is famous for his cow pie munching Desperate Dan in The Dandy, he was also instrumental in the launch of The Topper and The Beezer, illustrating Mickey the Monkey and Ginger, who was very similar to Watkins' other well-known character, Oor Wullie.

Jimmy AND HIS MAGIC PATCH

"KING ALFRED'S Camp," Jimmy Watson read as he cycled past a lonely signpost on his way to deliver some laundry. "I'll bet that was a long time ago," our pal mused. "Wish I'd lived here then!"

2—WHOOSH! Straightaway the Magic Patch sewn on Jimmy's trousers granted his wish—and our pal and his bike were back in the year 896! Nearby was King Alfred's camp. Suddenly, Jimmy gave a start.

3—Ahead were the dim figures of three Danish invaders! "I must warn King Alfred!" gasped our pal. Like a jet, he passed the startled Danes and sped down into the camp. "The Danes are here!" he roared.

4—The uproar brought King Alfred from his tent. Sword upraised, he saw Jimmy. "Halt!" he cried. Just then the loosely-held spear of a soldier caught in the spokes of Jimmy's front wheel. That did it!

5—The bike stopped dead, and our pal, caught by surprise, was hurled over the handlebars to crash his head smack against the King's chin. It was at that moment the Danes staged their surprise attack.

6—The Saxon soldiers put up a brave fight, but were sorely outnumbered. Soon they were driven back. Hidden in a clump of bushes, Jimmy saw the half-dazed King being dragged off by his Danish captors.

Watkins was not limited to one-page humour comics; he also illustrated the boisterous pages of Jimmy and his Magic Patch, an adventure story about a boy whose patch transported him to many different times, places, and troubles!

7—No sooner had the Danes gone than Jimmy set to work. The laundry package had burst open and had given our pal an idea. Using a Danish helmet he found, and the white sheets, he rigged up a fearful-looking monster with two bicycle lamps as "eyes."

8—"It was my fault the King was captured," muttered Jimmy determinedly, as he jumped into the saddle, under the white sheet draped over his cycle. "And it's my job to rescue him!" Cycling quickly, he soon saw, ahead of him, the Danish kidnappers.

9—Through the eyeholes that he had made in the sheet Jimmy saw that the Danes had tied King Alfred to a stake. As he neared the Danes, Jimmy gave a blood-curdling shriek. That was enough! The terror-stricken invaders fled and Jimmy freed the King.

10—There wasn't a second to lose. Quickly showing the grateful King how to perch on the handlebars, Jimmy leapt into the saddle and they were off! Bumpetty-bump-bump! But the Danes had tumbled to the trick and were in pursuit of the escaping pair.

11—As Jimmy pedalled madly through the Danes' horse lines the horses broke loose and fled. King Alfred knew he was slowing the speed of the bicycle, and he took a desperate chance. Just as a galloping horse passed he made a daring leap into its saddle.

12—His load lightened, Jimmy shot off after the King's mount like greased lightning. The pair were soon met by the re-formed Saxon Army. "To battle!" roared King Alfred, brandishing his sword. Grimly Jimmy brandished his bicycle pump in approval.

13—But before the advance on the Danes could be made, the soldiers' weapons had to be sharpened. It would have been a slow job if Jimmy hadn't been around! With the rear wheel of his bike geared to a farmhouse grindstone, our pal trod on the pedals.

14—The grindstone spun round, and in a matter of minutes the spears and swords were razor-sharp. At last the army moved off, led by the King on his white horse and Jimmy on his bike. It was not long before they were halted at the edge of a fast-flowing river.

15—Part of the river's narrow bridge had been washed away. Here was another job for Jimmy and his bike! Pedalling like fury, our pal sped down on to the bridge, zoomed into the air, and made a perfect landing on the other side. The watching men cheered.

16—Grinning, Jimmy jumped from the saddle. "Throw me a rope!" shouted the lad. "You tie one end to a tree and I'll do the same here. Then you'll be able to swing across!" Jimmy's plan worked a treat, and soon the army was safely over the water.

17—The Danes were drawn up for battle in a nearby field. When Alfred, on horseback, gave the order to advance, Jimmy was by his side. His bike was loaded with spare arrows, and jutting out from the handle-bars was a spear. Jimmy was ready for action.

18—The two armies met in a clash of steel and a furious battle raged. Guiding his way through the enemy's ranks, Jimmy suddenly felt a thud on the carrier of his bike. Behind him was a big, hulking Dane, his raised sword ready to strike down our pal!

19—Just then another Dane darted in to attack Jimmy from the front. Pulling hard on his brakes, Jimmy made his back wheel shoot up into the air, and the Dane on the carrier was shot from his perch to crash his sword down upon the head of his warlike pal.

20—With his two attackers lying senseless on the ground, Jimmy was free to speed around the lines of Saxon archers and hand out his supplies of spare arrows. Under the deadly hail of arrows the defeated Danes retreated to their ships, moored near the beach.

21—By the time the Saxon force reached the beach the two Danish ships were in full sail and the last of the enemy were struggling aboard. Just then Jimmy's eyes fell on a bucket of pitch left by the raiders. Quickly he dipped a spear into the thick, black tar.

22—Another spear was treated in the same way, then both the pitch-covered spear-heads were set alight. Mounting his bike, Jimmy set off with them through the surf. Braving a shower of spears, he hurled his " fire-spears " into the sails of the escaping ships.

23—In a minute the dry sails were a mass of flames. As the Danes jumped overboard, Alfred's men were waiting on the beach to take them prisoner. After the King had praised Jimmy for his part in the great victory the march inland began. What a laugh !

24—Swopping his bike for King Alfred's white horse, Jimmy played a merry tune on his mouth-organ while the King wobbled along on the lad's bike. And before the Magic Patch whisked our pal back to modern times, King Alfred had safely passed his test !

LORD SNOOTY AND HIS PALS

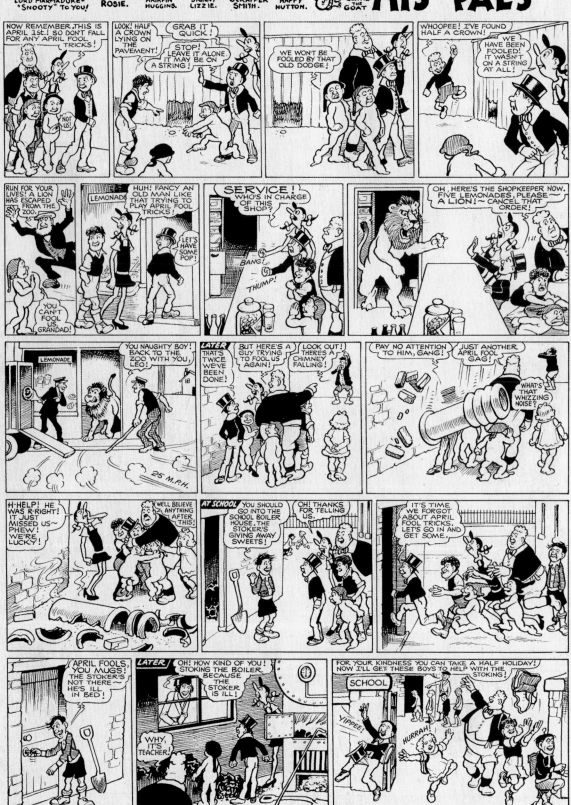

LORD SNOOTY AND HIS PALS

Malcolm Judge

Malcolm Judge's DC Thomson career catapulted to success in 1960. From then onwards, he flew into working on other titles such as Ali and his Baba for Sparky, Square Eyes for The Topper, Billy Whizz for Beano, along with many, many others!

ALI AND HIS BABA

HE HAS AN INVISIBLE BODYGUARD!

the NUMSKULLS

the NUMSKULLS

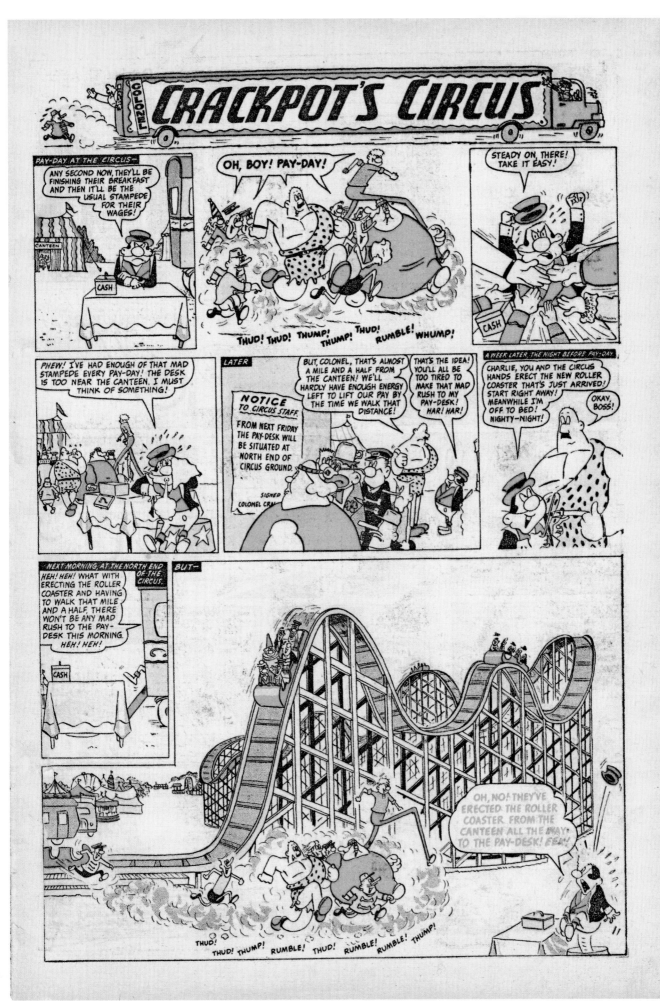

Although short-lived, Buzz, DC Thomson's broadsheet humour comic, was graced with the cover stars Hop, Skip and Jock.
The terrible threesome were the only ones ever to star on the cover and were drawn by Mal Judge!

The Beezer's Badd Lads were a gang of three bumbling crooks; Fingers the thin moustachioed spiv, Knuck the dim-witted heavy, and Boss the titchy mastermind whose schemes always ended up putting him behind bars!

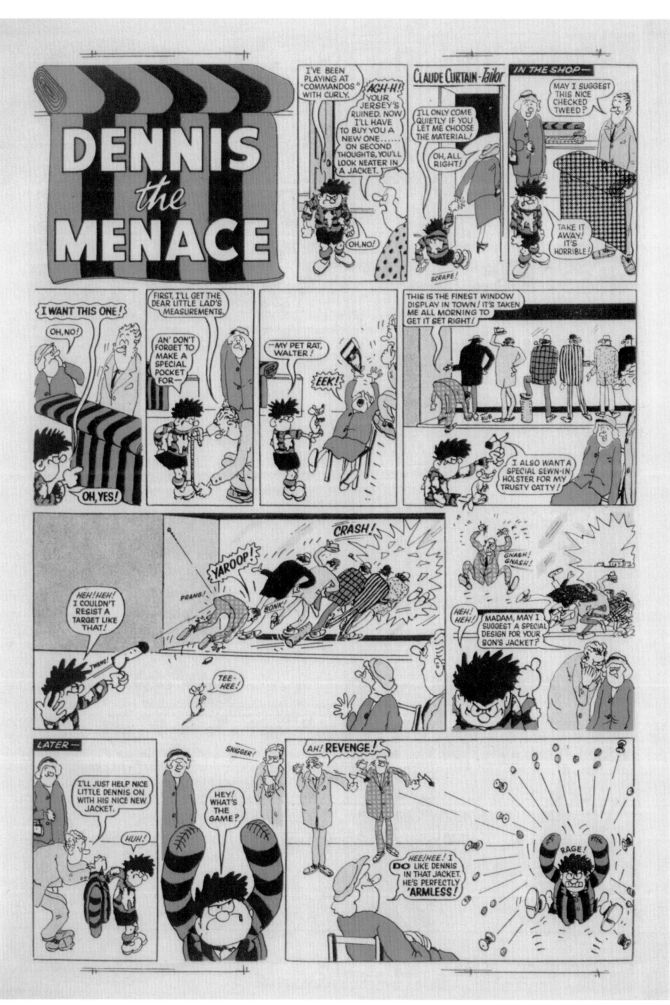

David Law

When Davey Law hit British comics, he hit it hard and with a home run. Working on Beano, Law ushered in a new, anti-establishment style of comics with a new character whose reign of terror has not ended yet!

The Colonel goes "Crack!"—And his gun shoots tack-tack!

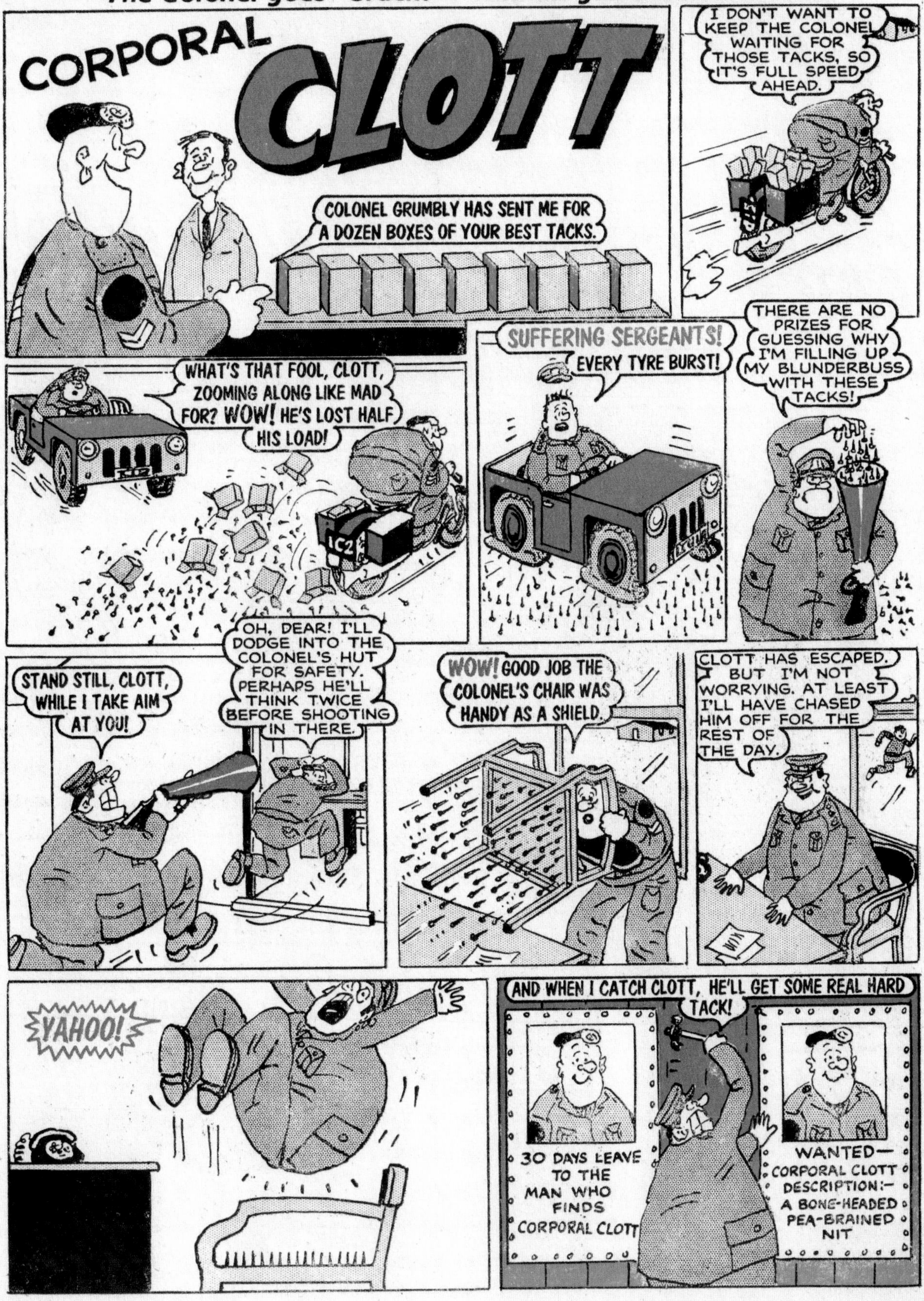

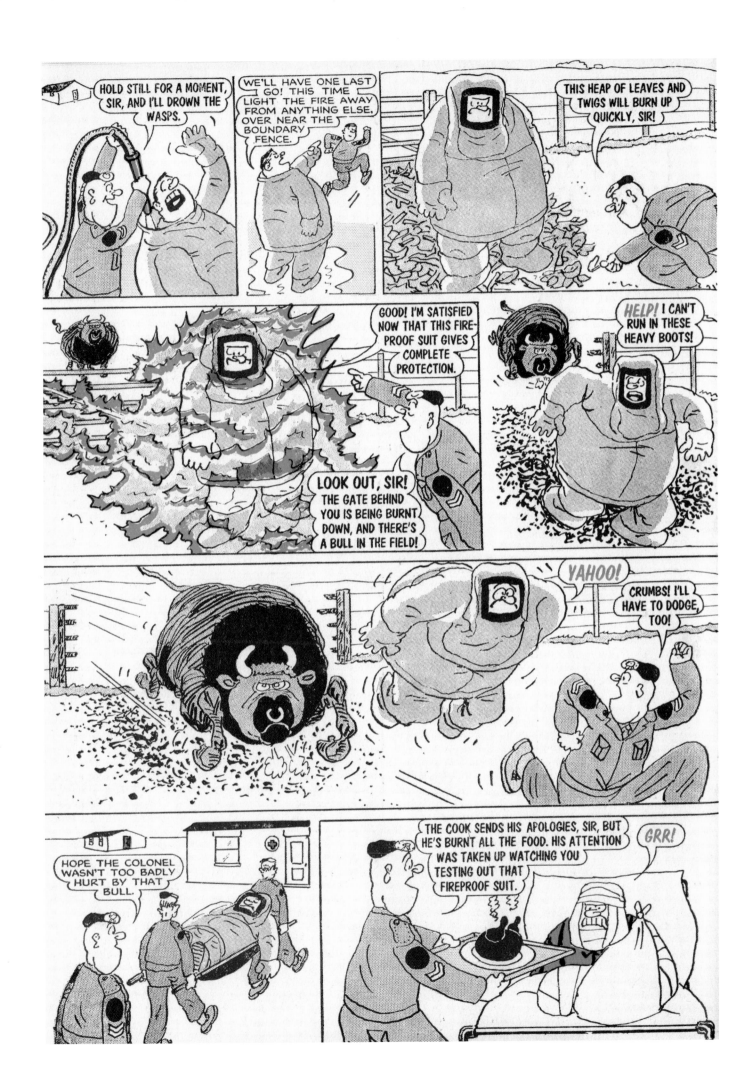

DENNIS the MENACE

Cover star of The Topper, only mess with Beryl at your own peril! In this sausage-y sojourn from 1960,
Beryl has a butcher's hook at sausage-making – much to the butcher's dismay!
Serves him right for knocking her money down the drain!

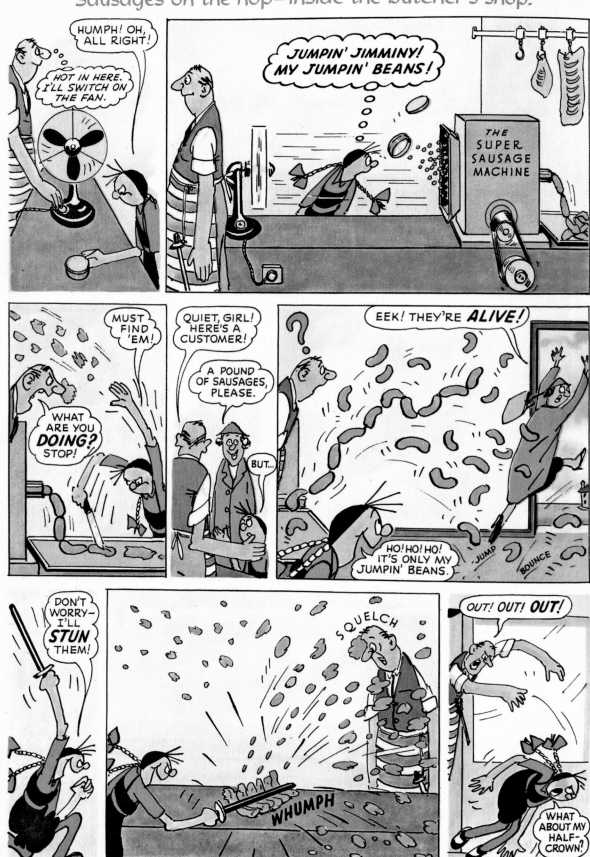

There's a splintering crash—when she pays in hard cash!

David Sutherland

Prolific artist David Sutherland has had a long career at DC Thomson. Among his many exploits, Sutherland has taken over great scripts from great artists like Leo Baxendale's Bash Street Kids – a strip he still draws to this day.

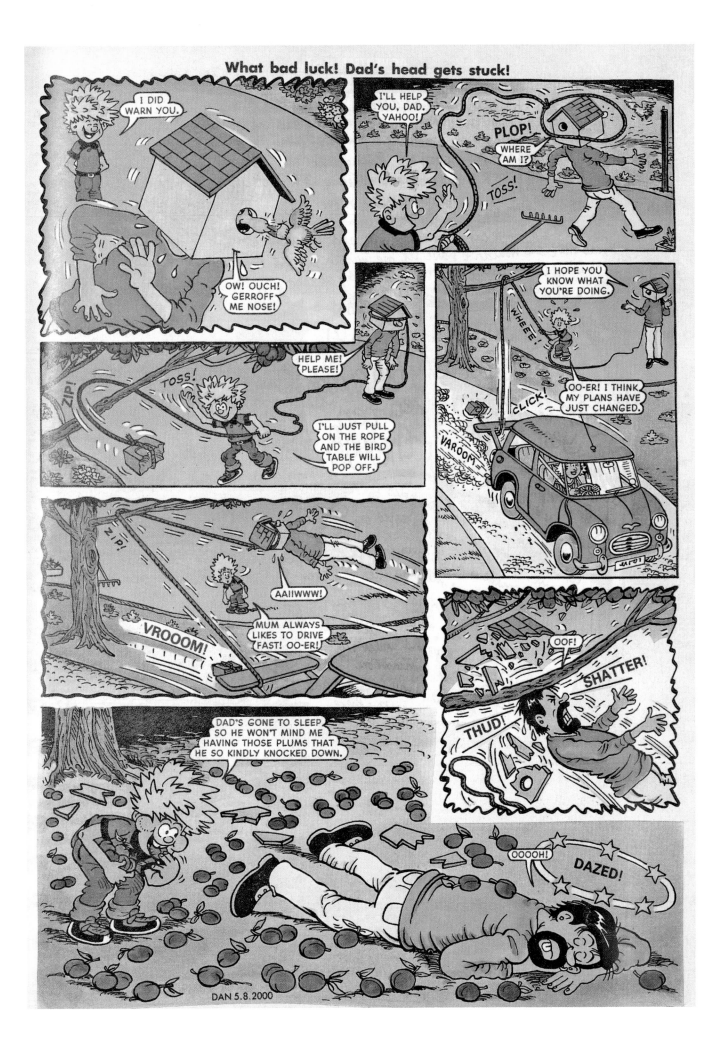

After becoming the lead artist on the Menace, David Sutherland was the obvious choice for Dennis's horror of a hound's own strip; Gnasher's Tale. The yarns followed Gnasher's exploits as a puppy and in this tale, the pup convinces an Old English Sheepdog to get a new look that leaves him feeling sheepish!

BILLY the CAT

THE amazing story of a strange acrobatic boy who roams the rooftops of Burnham, seeking out criminals and bringing them to justice . .

But Billy could turn his talents to things other than crime-fighting. One day in the High Street—

WHAT'S THAT HELICOPTER DOING OVER BURNHAM?

THERE HE IS! THERE'S BILLY THE CAT!

ATTENTION, BILLY THE CAT— STAND BY TO BE PICKED UP!

GOSH! WONDER WHAT THEY WANT?

Billy decided to take a chance . . .

OK! UP WE GO!

The helicopter crew would give no reason for inviting Billy aboard and shortly afterwards the machine landed at Beaton Hill, the nearby R.A.F. aerodrome.

HELLO, BILLY. I'M FLIGHT LIEUTENANT EDWARDS...

Flight Lieutenant Edwards quickly explained that the annual air display was being held, and asked if Billy would help. Soon . . .

. . AND NOW BILLY THE CAT!

Billy thrilled the spectators with a tremendous display of agility.

Group Captain Smythe, the Station Commander, was so enthralled that he took his private plane alongside the stunt plane to have a "ringside" view!

GOOD GRIEF! THAT MACHINE'S IN TROUBLE!

The aircraft burst into flames as Billy scrambled down from the top wing of his own plane.

FLY JUST ABOVE THE OTHER PLANE AS IT LANDS!

As Billy pulled the Group Captain from the blazing aircraft, his own pilot opened the throttle . . .

. . . just in time. The flames had reached the aircraft's fuel tanks.

R.A.F. TRAMPOLINE DISPLAY

R.A.F. TRAMPOLINE DISPLAY

LISTEN TO THE CROWDS CHEERING! THEY THOUGHT THAT WAS PART OF THE ACT!

Later that day, Billy was returned to his rooftops by a grateful R.A.F.

CRUMBS! WHAT A DAY! CATCHING CROOKS IS MUCH SAFER THOUGH!

Leo Baxendale

Giant of the British comics industry, Leo Baxendale was so influential that his impact can still be felt on comics to this day. Starting with Little Plum in 1952, Baxendale was so good that in less than two years he was given another four strips.

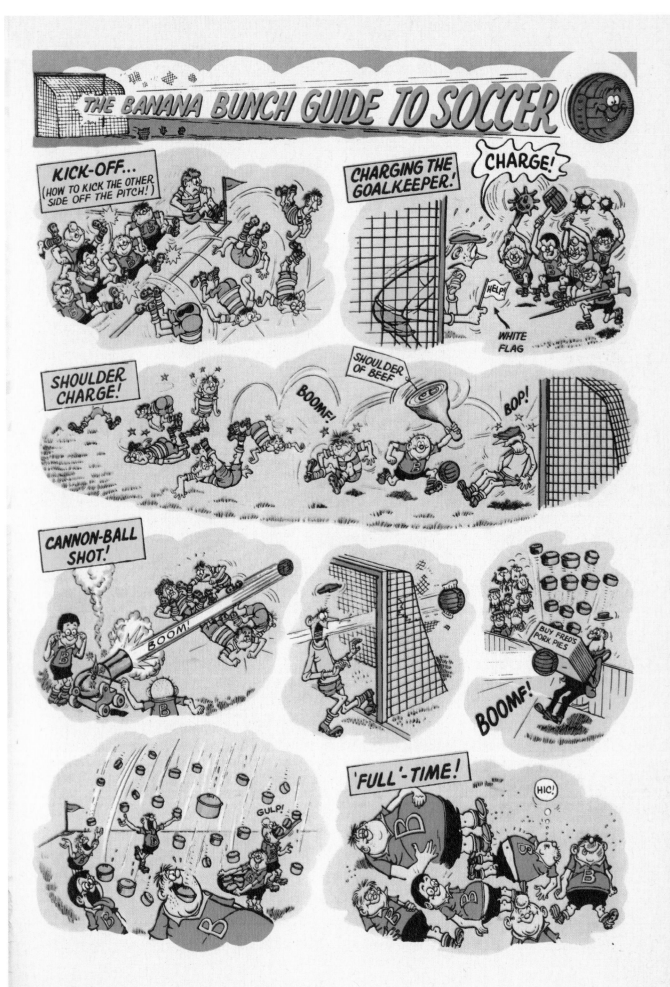

Allan Morley | Keyhole Kate, Freddy the Fearless Fly, and Hungry Horace – all these titles have something in common: Allan Morley! So beloved was Morley that RD Low said that if anything happened to the Morley fun factory then the comics might be forced to close.

If the dog had barked another once — It wouldn't have become a dunce!

Hungry Horace solves a puzzle — So now he can guzzle!

Hear Roger grunt and groan under the weight of a huge milestone!

Ken Reid

Ken Reid was a force to be reckoned with in the British comics industry – much like his influential characters, Roger the Dodger and Jonah. His flair for the funnies made him a much sought after artist.

Cecil comes to play with Roger — but he's another artful dodger!

ROGER the DODGER

MUM AND I ARE OFF FOR THE DAY, ROGER. YOU AND CECIL CAN DO THE HOUSEWORK— AND NO DODGING!

SNORT! HUH!

 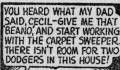 
YOU HEARD WHAT MY DAD SAID, CECIL—GIVE ME THAT 'BEANO', AND START WORKING WITH THE CARPET SWEEPER. THERE ISN'T ROOM FOR TWO DODGERS IN THIS HOUSE!

HUH! IS THAT SO! WELL, I'LL ANNOY HIM SO MUCH THAT HE'LL BE GLAD TO GIVE ME BACK THAT 'BEANO'!

OOPS! SORRY, ROGER! THE SWEEPER SLIPPED.

THAT'S ALL RIGHT, CECIL. JUST CARRY ON.

BAH! I'VE SWEPT THE WHOLE FLOOR, AND HE'S STILL READING! —I'LL HAVE TO TRY ANOTHER DODGE.

SORRY IF I'M IN YOUR LIGHT, ROGER—BUT I'VE GOT TO CLEAN THE WINDOWS.

NEVER MIND, CECIL. I'LL JUST WAIT UNTIL YOU'VE FINISHED.

CECIL FOLLOWS ROGER INTO THE GARDEN

PARDON THE DUST, ROGER—BUT I HAVE TO CLEAN THE CARPET.

CARRY ON, CECIL. I DON'T MIND THE DUST.

TWO HOURS LATER

HE! HE! THANKS FOR DOING ALL THOSE JOBS WHILE TRYING TO ANNOY ME, CECIL —NOW I CAN GO TO MY BEDROOM AND READ 'THE BEANO' IN PEACE!

GR-R-R!

GRRR! ROGER HAS LOCKED HIMSELF IN HIS ROOM BUT HE WON'T GET PEACE FOR LONG IF I CAN HELP IT!

TUG

OUTSIDE ROGER'S WINDOW

ROAD WORKS

B-R-R-R

I'LL LEAD THE GUIDE STRINGS PAST THE WINDOW, AND THE WORKMEN WILL FOLLOW WITH THEIR DRILLS.

5 MINUTES LATER

HA! HA! YOU'LL HAVE TO THINK OF A BETTER DODGE THAN THAT CECIL - I'VE STUCK COTTON WOOL IN MY EARS!

BAH! I GIVE UP! I'M GOING HOME!

TWO HOURS LATER

MUM AND DAD SHOULD BE HOME ANY MINUTE NOW! HELP!

CHUG! CHUG! CHUG! CHUG!

UNKNOWN TO THE TWO DODGERS, THE WORKMEN WERE BEING FOLLOWED BY A MECHANICAL SHOVEL —

CHUG CHUG

AND WHEN MUM AND DAD COME HOME

HURRY UP AND FILL IN THIS TRENCH—SO I CAN GET ACROSS—AND GET AT YOU!

Y-YES, DAD, ONLY ANOTHER THREE TONS TO SHOVEL.

You may think there's a curse on this comic but it's just Jonah's habitual bad luck! For a time, the star-crossed sailor was written by Walter Fearn whose scripts Ken Reid found hilarious, despite making his own slight visual adjustments!

Tom Paterson

The legendary Tom, or Tam, Paterson began drawing for Beano in the 1980s. He modelled much of his artistic style on Leo Baxendale's artwork, with large and detailed depictions of mayhem alongside a large splash of gross-out humour!

THE BANANA BUNCH

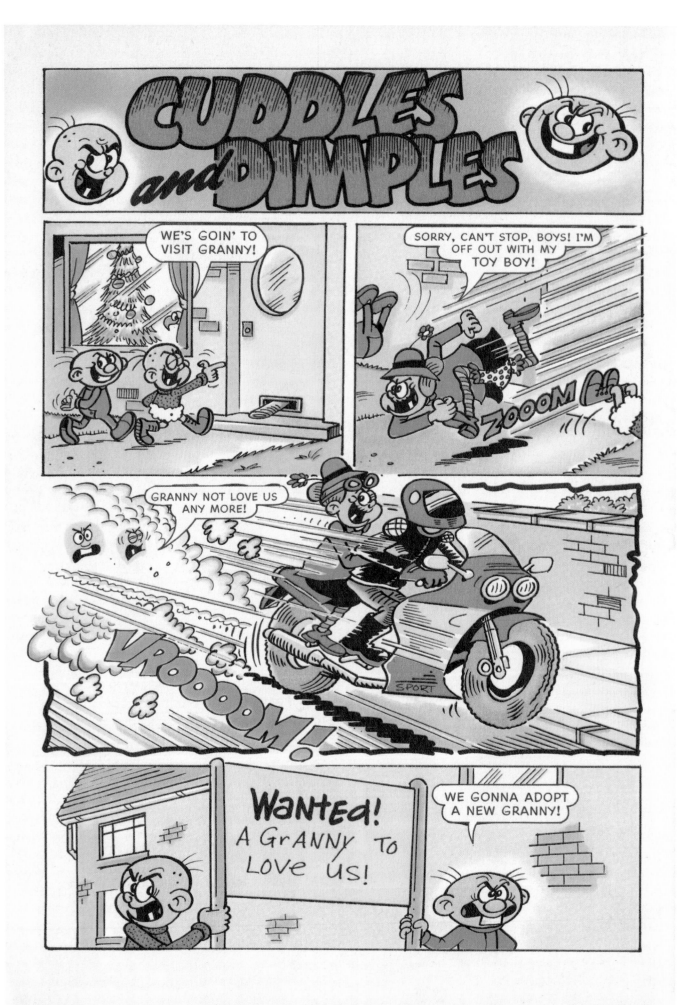

Barrie Appleby

Barrie Appleby joined the Beano gang in the 1970s, drawing regular strips for Dennis the Menace and Roger the Dodger, as well as disobedient duo Cuddles and Dimples for The Dandy, but is probably best known for his run of Bananaman.

BANANAMAN

YAWN! WELL, I'VE HAD A BIT OF A LONG LIE, BUT, HEY — THAT'S WHAT SATURDAYS ARE FOR!

But when Eric opens the curtains...

HEY! WHY'S IT STILL DARK OUTSIDE?

I COULDN'T HAVE SLEPT RIGHT THROUGH TILL ELEVEN O'CLOCK AT NIGHT, COULD I?

Then...

WHO'S PHONING ME AT THIS TIME OF DAY... OR NIGHT???

DRRING!

It's Chiefy.

I'VE GOT SOME BAD NEWS FOR BANANAMAN, ERIC. ASK HIM TO COME TO THE STATION — RIGHT AWAY.

WANTED

NO SOONER SAID THAN DONE, CHIEFY.

When little Eric eats a banana...

FAZZ...

OOOMF!

DAN.4.3.2000

...he turns into BANANAMAN!

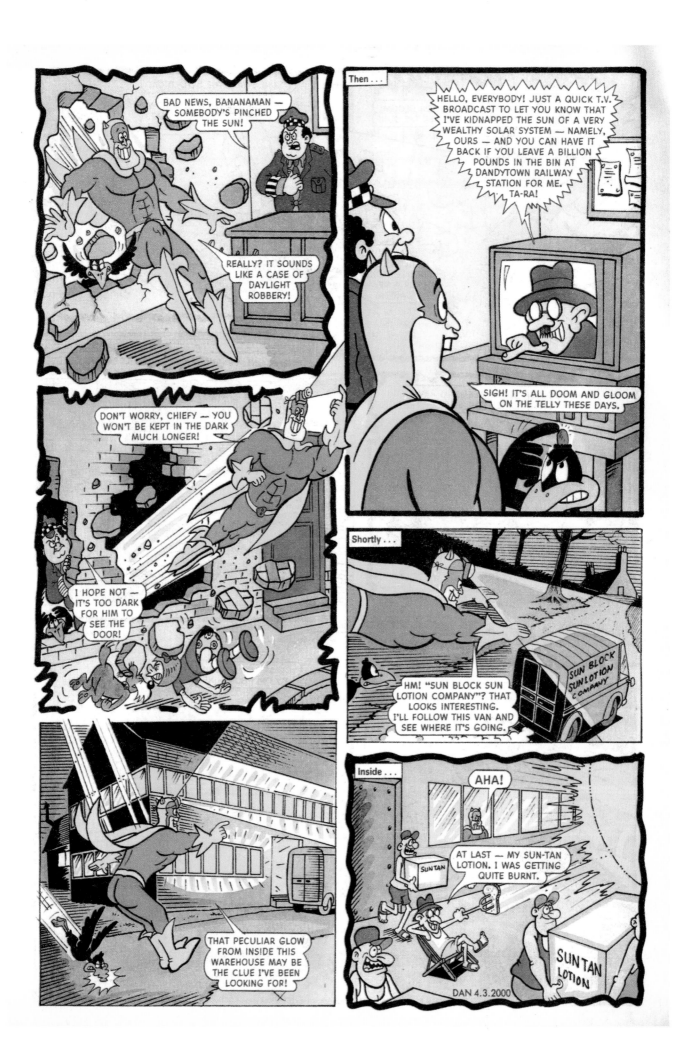

CURLY'S COMMANDOS

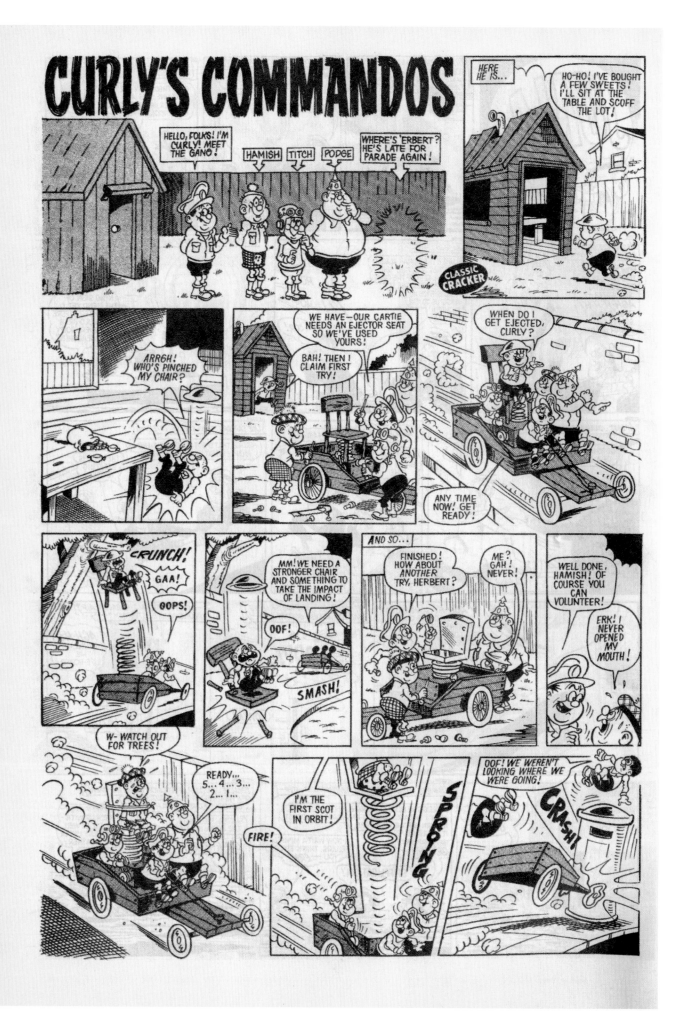

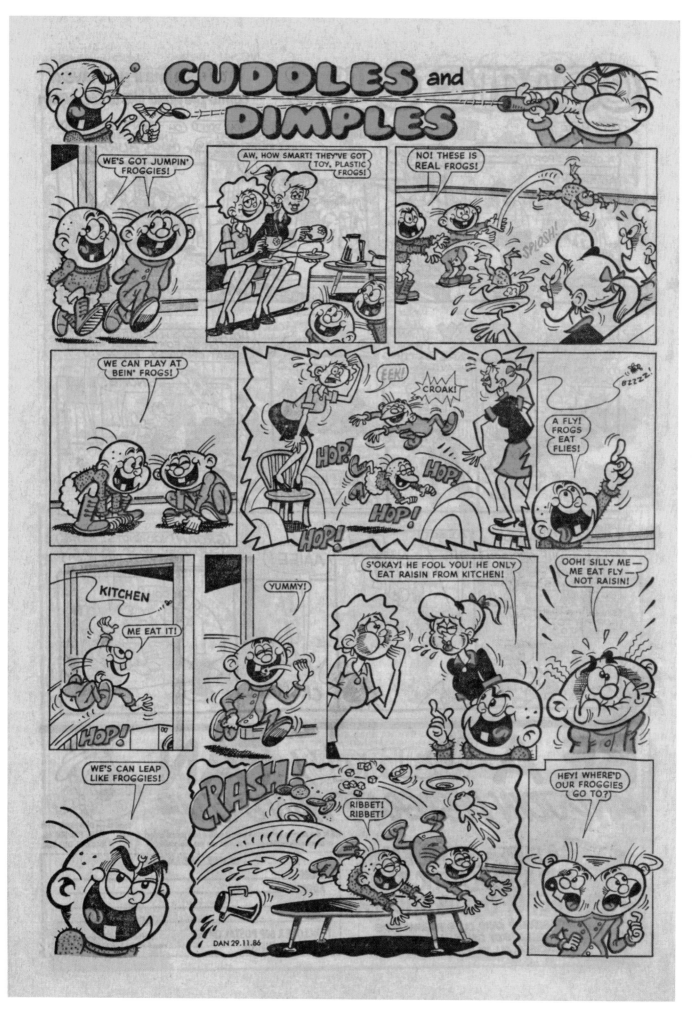

CUDDLES and DIMPLES

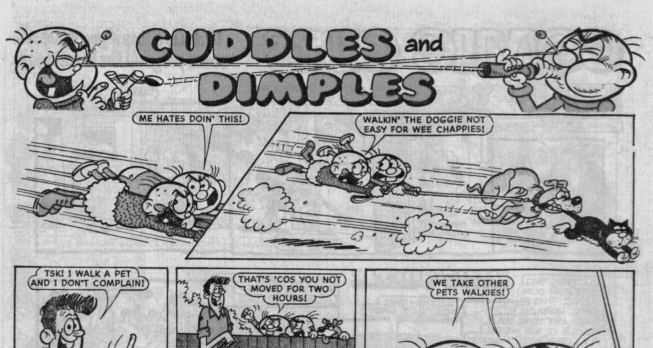

DAN 13.12.86

Jim Petrie Jim Petrie was Beano Editor Harry Cramond's first choice to take over drawing Minnie the Minx from Leo Baxendale. While mainly providing inks, he also produced some outstanding coloured spreads, always making sure they had Minx appropriate big splashes of red!

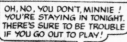

As well as being one of the regular crew at Beano, Jim Petrie also worked on other titles including The Beezer, for which he drew the vexatious Little Mo.

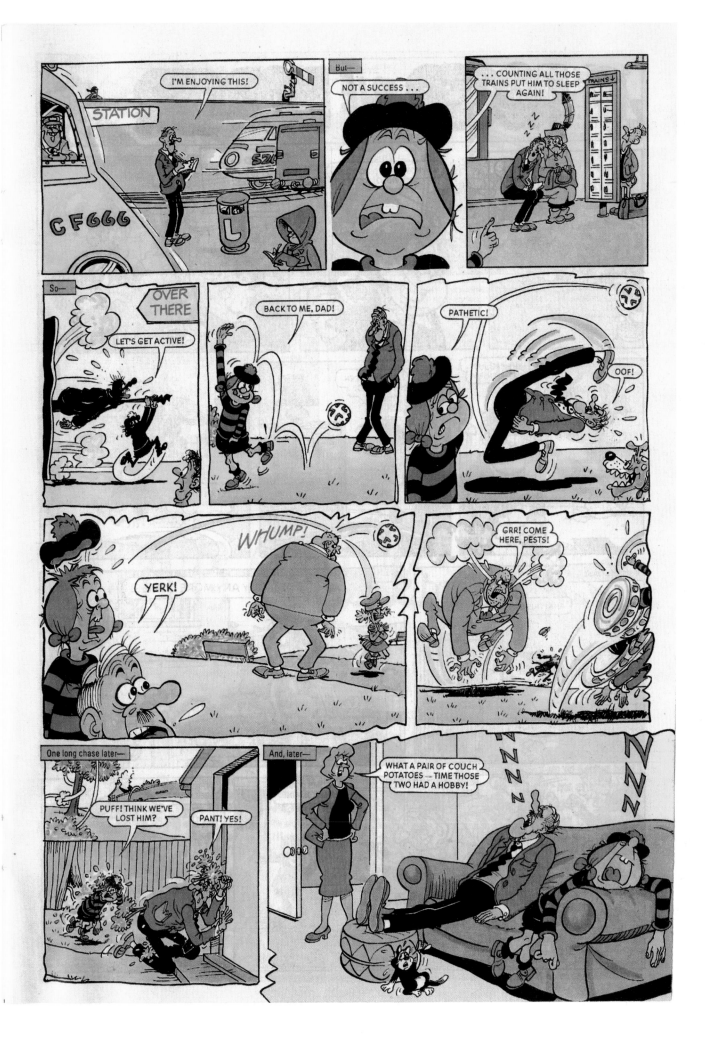

LAUGHS FOR ALL WITH A BOUNCING BALL.

YOUNG SID

George Martin | With his fingers in all the pies, George Martin worked on most of DC Thomson's humour comics, producing work for Nutty, The Dandy, The Topper, The Beezer, Buzz, Sparky, and Hoot! He really did chortle with chums!

Art's always playing jokes—with his clever pencil strokes.

Art's trick is neat—he's too smart for Pete.

CLAUDE HOPPER

Meet the lad with the wildest cat in the world!

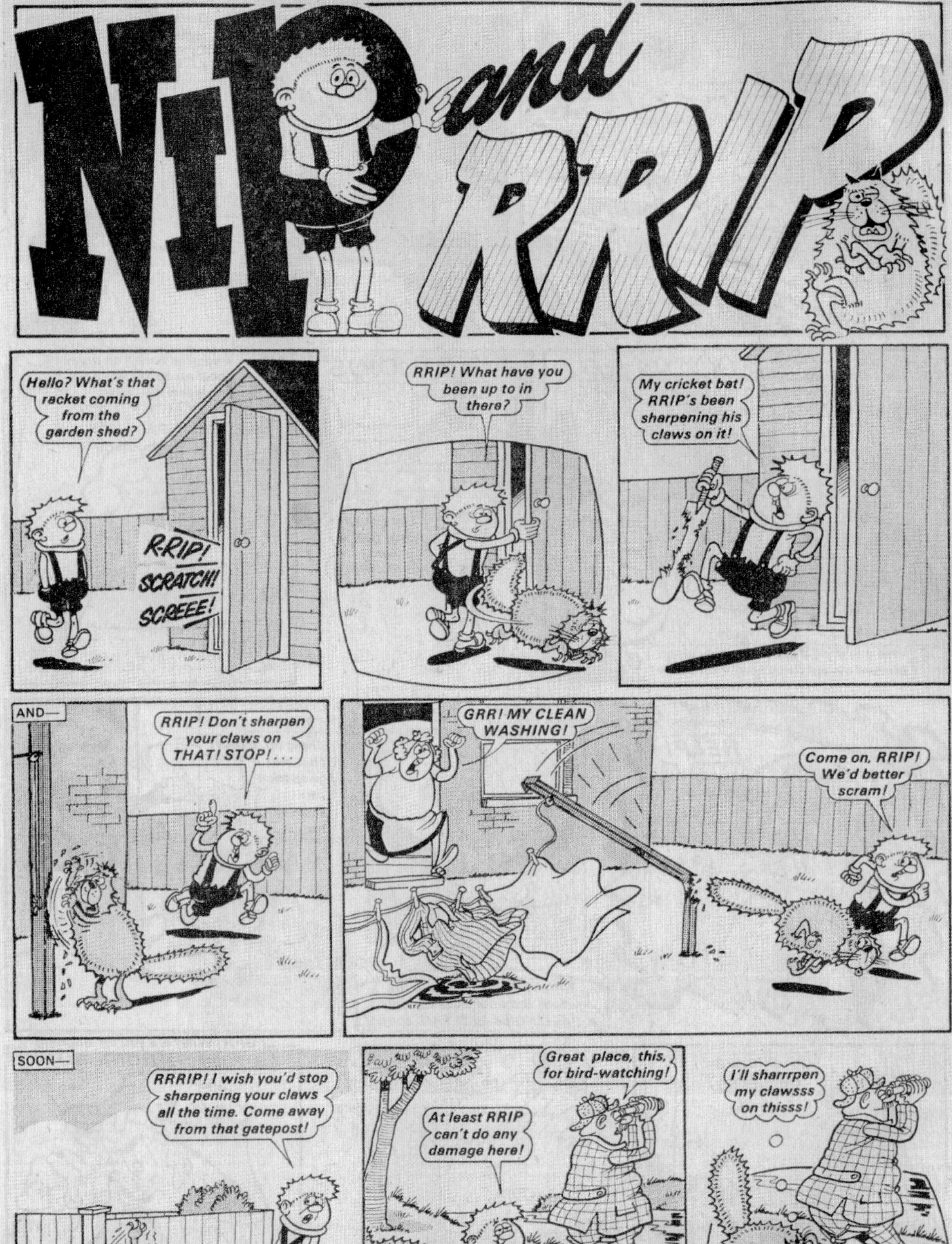

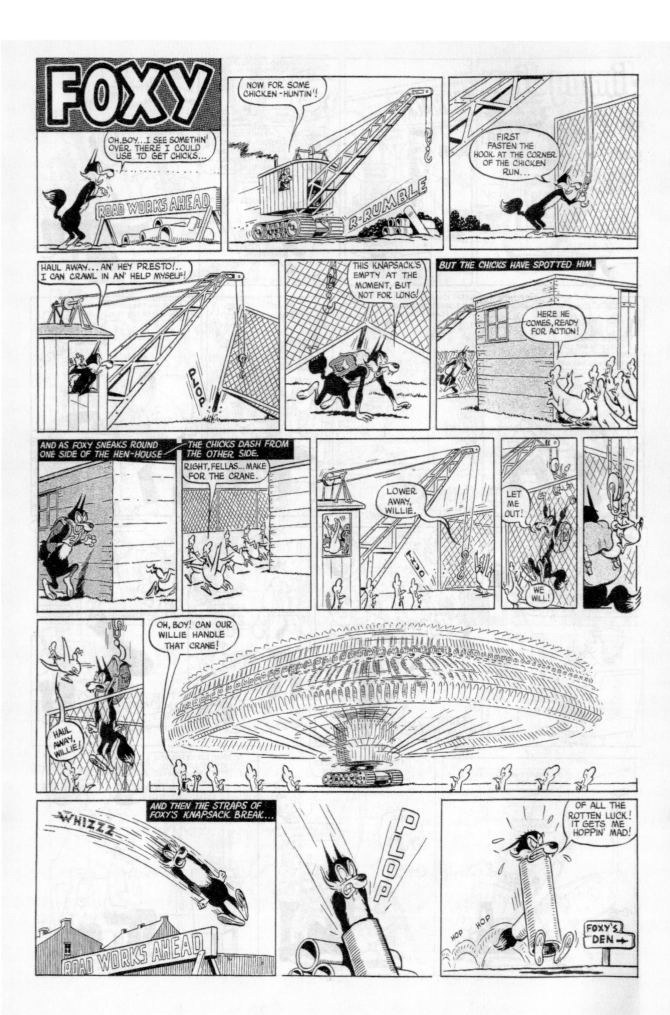

What has a head but no eyes? — A pin!

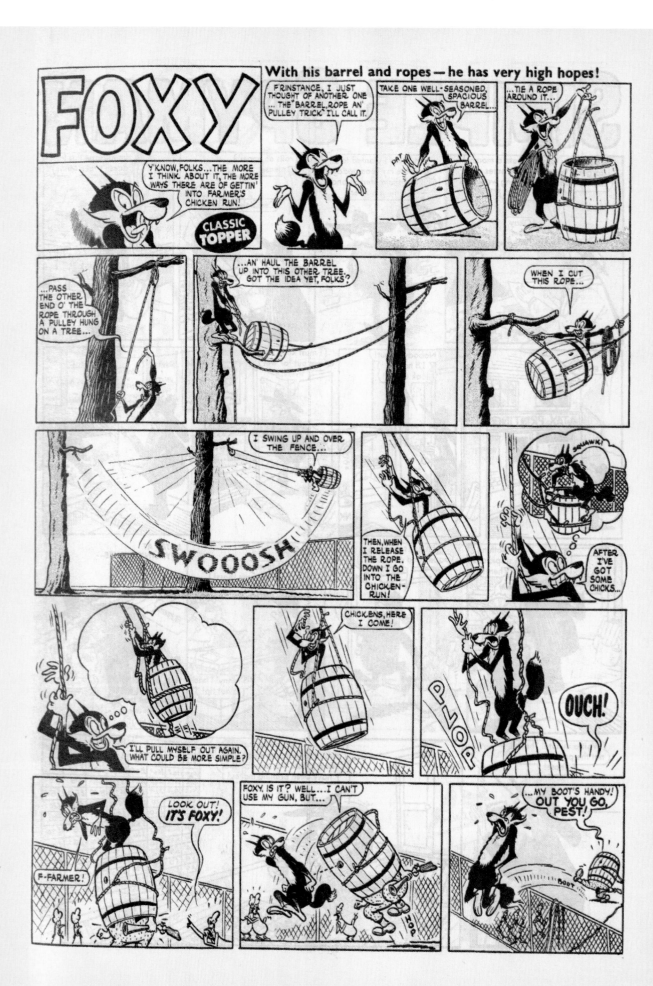

A shock for Tom Cat—when his plan falls flat.

Martin also created the beloved Julius Cheeser for The Topper, a tumultuous cat and mouse duo akin to Tom and Jerry, with hilarious results.

JULIUS CHEESER

LIFE'S SURE GRIM WHEN THEY GO FOR A SWIM!

THE HILLYS AND THE BILLYS

THE BILLYS HAVE STARTED FEUDIN' MIGHTY EARLY TODAY!

IT'S THE BILLYS!

THEY'RE EVERYWHERE!

LATER, WHEN THE SHOOTIN' DIES DOWN, THE HILLYS GET TO WORK—DIGGIN' IN!

TOMORROW WE'LL BE WAITIN' FOR 'EM—IN OUR TRENCH!

NEXT DAY

C'MON, LADS—INTO TH' TRENCH BEFORE THEM BILLYS ARRIVE!

SPLOSH!

WE THOUGHT YOU MIGHT PREFER A MOAT! HO! HO!

THEY'VE FILLED OUR TRENCH WITH WATER!

HEY, PAW! OUR SHOOTIN' IRONS IS STILL IN TH' WATER, AN' WE CAN'T GET 'EM WHILE THEM BILLYS IS STILL OUT THERE!

NO, BUT WE KIN DRAIN THE TRENCH FROM THE REAR!

THEM HILLYS IS TOO SCARED TO COLLECT THEIR GUNS—C'MON, FELLAHS! LET'S GET 'EM!

CHARGE!

PLOP!

WELL! WELL! LOOK AT THIS BUNCH O' STICK-IN-THE-MUDS! THEY DIDN'T KNOW WE'D DRAINED TH' MOAT!

HO! HO! HERE'S MUD IN YORE EYE!

Nigel Parkinson

Liverpudlian illustrator Nigel Parkinson's talents have graced both Beano and The Dandy on big names like Minnie the Minx and Cuddles and Dimples, which helped him land the role of official artist of Dennis the Menace in 2012.

SOUND EFFECTS — BAY 12

SOUND OF PIECE OF CHEESE

SOUND OF ONE HAND CLAPPING

SOUND OF THE CROWD

SOUND OF BABY CRYING

SOUND OF MEOWING CAT

SOUND OF BARKING DOG

SOUND OF SQUAWKING PARROT

SOUNDS LIKE SWINGTIME

SOUND OF RUNNING WATER

SOUND OF SOCKFUL OF CUSTARD

SOUND AS A POUND

SOUND OF BOOTS ON GRAVEL

SOUND OF DUCK QUACKING

SOUND OF LAUGHTER (I HOPE)

Wow! Look at all these other great sound effects.

A duck caller. What does it do?

Here's what!

QUACK!

QUACK!

THE NUMSKULLS

ALWAYS REMEMBER: ... ER...

My neighbour's on holiday, so I'm Bonzo-sitting for her.

Let's go in here, boy. I bet you'd love a bit of exercise.

THE PARK
CONTENTS:
GRASS
TREES
THAT'S ALL, REALLY!

HURTLE

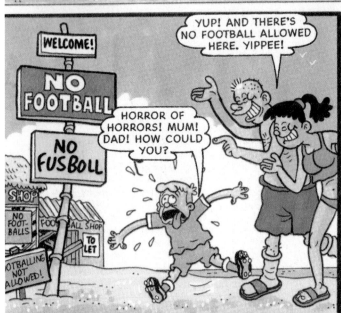

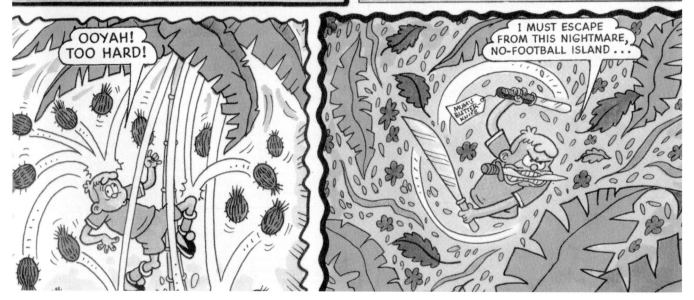

The BANANA BUNCH

What's wrong with Little Sis?

There's a spider inna Gang Hut!

You're not afraid of a teeny weensy spider, are you?

Yes . . .

. . . And you're afraid of a teensy weensy little sister, aren't you?

Ulp!

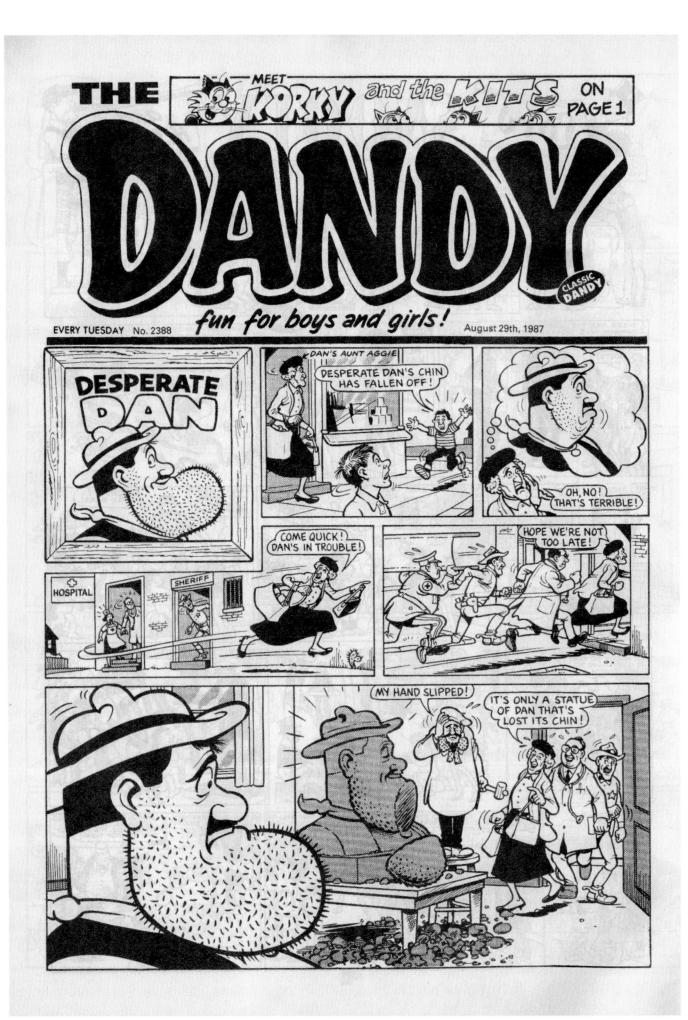

Ken H Harrison

Following in Dudley D Watkins' footsteps, several artists tried their hand at the chunky-chinned Desperate Dan, namely Ken Harrison. These were big boots to fill, as the cowboy was so famous in the UK that he was voted the public's second favourite superhero after Batman!

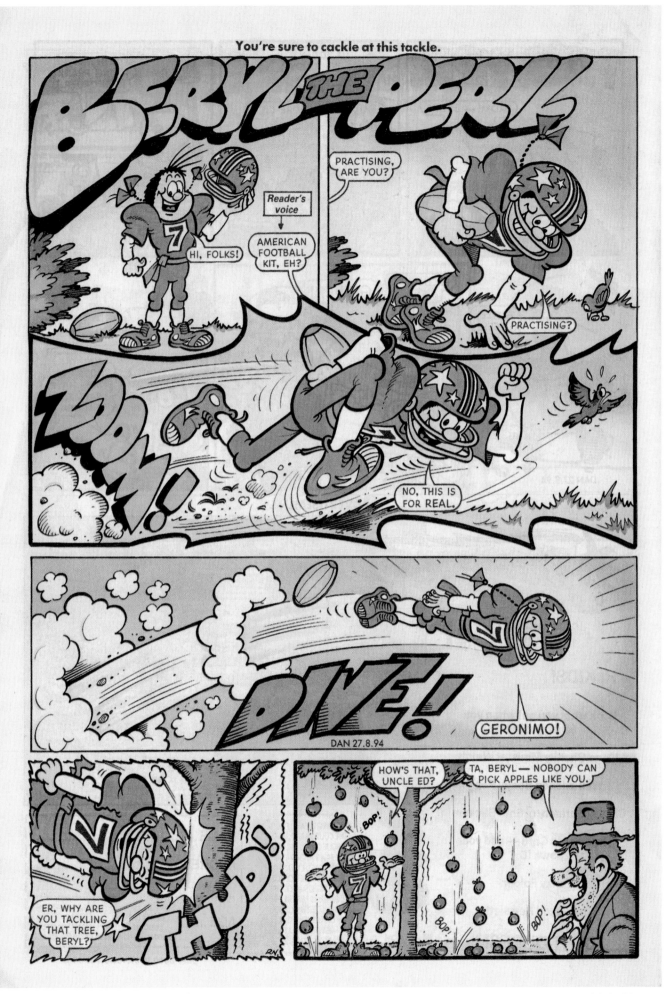

Robert Nixon

Robert Nixon started his illustrious career at DC Thomson with Beano's Little Plum in the 1960s and soon became the go-to-artist, taking over Roger the Dodger from Ken Reid and Lord Snooty from Dudley D Watkins.

In 1986, Nixon was chosen to take over from David Gudgeon drawing the cantankerous cat, changing the look of the character for the first time in forty years and adding his own spin by switching focus to the Kits — Nip, Lip and Rrip.

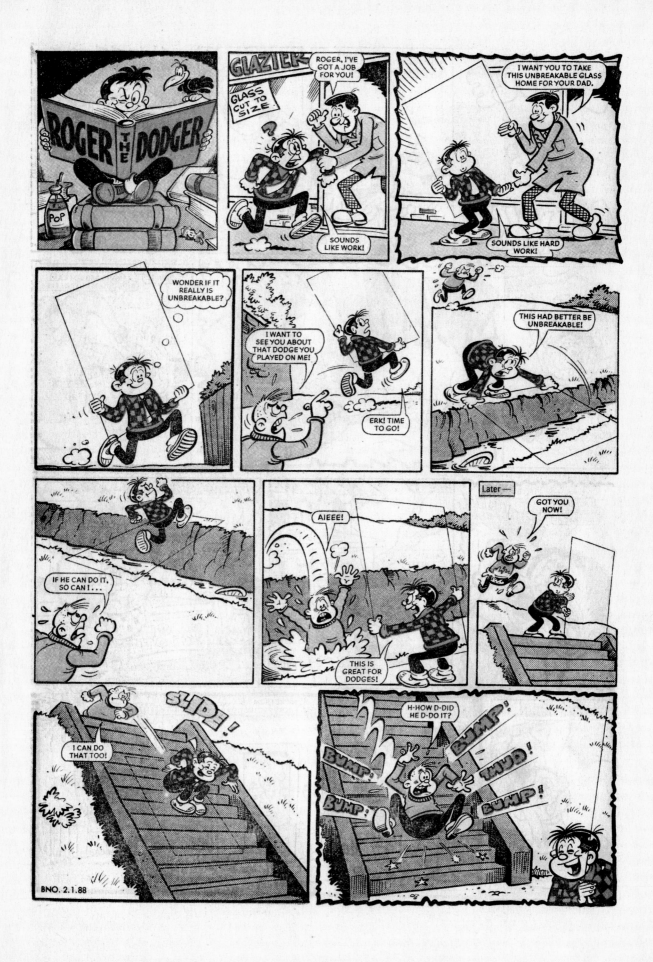

So there you have it, folks. We hope you had fun, and shared many a chortle with our chums — we know we did!

As you've seen, our zany bunch of characters (and their artists) never miss an opportunity for laughs, be it with George Martin's slapstick animal frenemies, or Ken Reid's grotesque gags, there's always something to tickle your funny bone and split your sides.

While our artists' work may have crossed many different titles, their humour is present in each and every strip, which, at the heart of it is what makes Beano, The Dandy and all their comic chums what they are today.